Devin Nunes 18+

Had A Farm

a satire by Ben Fletcher

First published in 2019 by Blue Lens

This edition published in 2020 by Toupee or Not Toupee

Toupee or Not Toupee is an imprint of Toupee or Not Toupee Limited

Toupee or Not Toupee Limited

85 Great Portland Street, 1st Floor

London, W1W 7LT, United Kingdom

Toupee or Not Toupee

1178 Broadway, 3rd Floor (#1329)

New York, NY 10001, United States

A CIP catalogue record for this book is available from the British Library

ISBN   978 1 914204 10 4

3 5 9 11 10 8 6 4 2

bensfletcher.com   @BenSFletcher

Printer and binder may vary between territories of production and sale

AND ON THAT FARM HE HAD A COW,
E-IGH, E-IGH, OH!

DEVIN NUNES HAD A FARM,
E-IGH, E-IGH, OH!

WITH A MOO OVER HERE,
AND A MOO OVER THERE...
IS THAT A COWPOKE IN YOUR POCKET?
HERE A MOO,
THERE A MOO,
EVERYWHERE A MOO!

DEVIN NUNES HAD A FARM,
E-IGH, E-IGH, OH!

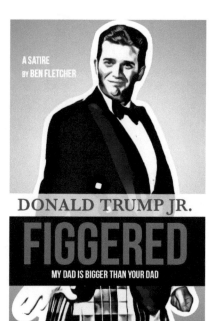